HEATHCLIFF

WANTED

by George Gately

D0868915

**tempo
books**
GROSSET & DUNLAP
A Filmways Company
Publishers • New York

WANTED:

Name: Heathcliff
Height: 13 inches
Weight: 12 pounds
Color: Orange
Distinguishing Characteristic: Able to create hilarity at the drop of a fishbowl.
Crimes: Fish robbery in the first degree
      Excessive garbage can dumping
      Impersonating a dog catcher
      Scratch post scuttling
      Bulldog baiting
      Milk truck marauding

Warning: This cat is armed with humor and may be dangerous to your funny bone.

"SAY!....YOU LOOK FAMILIAR!...."

"WHY CAN'T WE HAVE A DUMB OL' MASCOT LIKE ANY OTHER TEAM?!"

"ANYONE CARE FOR AN HORS D'OEUVRE?"

"THERE'S SOMEONE HERE TO SEE THE HEAD OF THE HOUSEHOLD!"

"CATS DON'T GET AN ALLOWANCE!"

"AWW!...DIDUMS FALL DOWN AND GO BOOM?!"

"PUT THAT BACK ... WHERE YOU GOT IT!"

"YOUR CAT IS QUITE A RETRIEVER!"

"...AND HOW MUCH WOULD YOU CHARGE FOR THIS ENDORSEMENT?"

"HE NEVER ACCEPTS FOURTH RUNNER-UP!"

"THEY'D LIKE A SET OF MATCHED SCRATCHING POSTS."

"HEATHCLIFF HAS SET UP A KITTEN CROSSING!"

"I CAN'T FIND THE COOKING SHERRY!"

"YOU ARE ABOUT TO THRASH SOMEONE TO A PULP!"

I'D BETTER NOT FIND ANY SCRATCHES ON THAT CUCKOO!

FIRST AID

"HOLD THE TUNA FISH!"

" STICK....

....'EM UP!"

"HE'S A VERY AGGRESSIVE MASCOT!"

"HE'S GOT A DUMPING PERMIT!"

"I SEE....AND WHERE ELSE DOES IT HURT?"

"HEAVENS!...I'LL BE GLAD WHEN WE GET
OUR NEW PICTURE TUBE!"

"YOUR SON, HEATHCLIFF, IS HERE TO SEE YOU."

"I THOUGHT THIS CLUB HAD AN EXCLUSIVE MEMBERSHIP!"

"A CATFISH IN THE WINDOW!...WHAT CATFISH?!"

"TONIGHT IT'S HIS BARBERSHOP QUARTET!"

"EVER GET THE FEELING SOMEONE IS
PEERING OVER YOUR SHOULDER?!"

© 1977
2-8 McNaught Synd., Inc.

"HEATHCLIFF HAS DECIDED TO MAKE PEACE."

"DO YOU REALIZE HOW MANY CAT FIGHTS
YOU'VE BEEN IN THIS WEEK?!"

"NEVER MIND USING THE CALCULATOR!!"

"ANY OTHER COLLATERAL?"

"WE'RE MISSING A PENGUIN!"

"I'M OUT!"   "I FOLD!"   "I QUIT!"

" YOU HAVEN'T WON IT YET! "

"I'M GLAD YOU ENJOYED THE SERMON."

"HEATHCLIFF HIRED A REFEREE."

"I'LL COMMENT ON THE REPORT CARD!"

"DOES HE ALWAYS INFLUENCE YOUR DECISIONS?"

"WOW!...WHAT HAPPENED TO YOU?!"

"THANKS, BUT I'LL PACK MY OWN LUNCH."

"ACE CAT FOOD COMPANY.... WHAT'S THAT, SIR?.."

"IT'S ONE OF HIS EARLY ANCESTORS WHO CHASED MICE FOR THE PIONEERS!"

"I'M VERY SORRY, BUT..."

"HE'D LIKE TO BORROW THE CAR TONIGHT."

"HEATHCLIFF!...GO HOME!"

"NICE TO SEE YOU, FRED...I'D BETTER GET BACK AND FINISH THE MARQUEE."

"I HATE TO DISTURB YOUR AFTER-DINNER NAP, BUT...."

"HE'S PATROLLING IN AN UNMARKED CAR!"

3-18

© 1977
McNaught Synd., Inc.

"ALL YOU BUMS!...OUTA THE PARK!!"

"YEAH!...YOU TOO!"

"BUT THE DENTED CAT FOOD CANS ARE ON SALE, DEAR!"

"HE'S BEEN VOTED GRAND EXALTED RULER
OF THE LOYAL ORDER OF ALLEY CATS!"

"HAH!...MY KITE'S HIGHER THAN YOURS!"

"TONIGHT, IT'S A HOOTENANNY!"

"LET ME EXPLAIN....THIS IS NOT THE ORIGINAL ARK..."

"HE'S MADE A POSITIVE IDENTIFICATION FROM THE MUG SHOTS!"

"YOU'LL HAVE TO REMOVE YOUR T-SHIRT."

"AH!...I'M JUST IN THE MOOD FOR A MIDNIGHT SNACK!"

"HAVE YOU BEEN AT THAT FISH TANK?!"

"WHO'S THE NEW GUY?"

"SORRY, SPIKE, BUT THE PASSWORD IS 'MEOW'!"

"HE DOESN'T LIKE IT WHEN I STAND AROUND AND GOSSIP."

"LET ME EXPLAIN THE MASCOT'S JOB...."

"THERE'S SOMEONE HERE ABOUT OUR CAT FOOD!"

"YOU'RE NO RAY OF SUNSHINE ON A MONDAY MORNING!"

"HAVE YOU SEEN A FOX, LITTLE GIRL?"

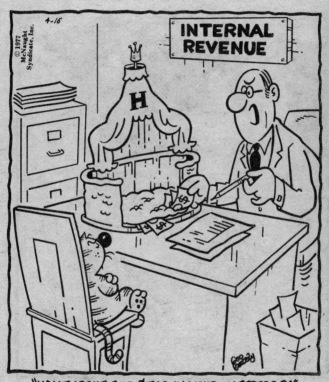

"WHAT ABOUT THIS $700 IN YOUR MATTRESS?!"

"HAVE DECIDED NOT TO TAKE PRISONERS!"

© 1977
McNaught
Syndicate, Inc.

"WE NEVER SHOULD HAVE ASKED HIM TO PLAY 'GO FISH'!"

"NOTICE, MADAM, HOW NICELY IT PICKS UP
THOSE DISGUSTING CAT HAIRS!"

© 1977
McNaught
Syndicate, Inc.

" HE'S VERY SENSITIVE."

"HEATHCLIFF BELIEVES IN A BIG ENTRANCE!"

"LET'S YOU AND I HAVE A LITTLE TALK..."

"NO, NO,
HEATHCLIFF!"

"G'WAN!...IT
LOOKS YUMMY!"

"WAIT 'TIL YOU SEE WHAT HE'S DONE WITH HIS SCRATCHING POST!"

"HE'S RUNNING OFF WITH THE GYPSIES!"

"IT'S CLEAN CHICKEN!...YOU DON'T HAVE TO WASH IT!"

"CRUNCH!"

"THERE *WAS* A HOT DOG IN IT WHEN I PASSED IT DOWN THE AISLE!"

"I THINK HE GOT A WHIPLASH!"

"REMEMBER, GENTLEMEN, OUR SENSATIONAL NEW CAT FOOD FORMULA MUST BE KEPT IN UTMOST SECRECY!"

"...AND THE VILLAGERS WORSHIPED THE GREAT STONE IDOL..."

"WHAT HAPPENED, SMOKEY?"

"HE SIGNED ON FOR A HITCH WITH THE TUNA FLEET!"

"DID YOU TRY A WHITE FLAG OF SURRENDER?"

"BENEATH HIS ROUGH EXTERIOR,
BEATS A HEART OF GOLD!"

"RESPONSIBLE OPPOSING VIEWS TO THIS EDITORIAL
WILL BE GRANTED EQUAL TIME TO REPLY..."

"EEYAH!!"

"WHERE'S OUR POLAR BEAR RUG?"

"HE'S PERFECTED A BREED OF LARGE, ROASTER PARAKEETS!"

"HE'S GOING TO WEAR OUT THAT COPY OF 'MOBY DICK'!"

"STOP!-THIEF!!"

"THIS IS GETTING SERIOUS!"

"OH, OH!...HE'S IN ONE OF HIS PLAYFUL MOODS!"

"PLASTIC CANS DON'T MAKE ENOUGH NOISE TO SUIT HIM!"

"LOOK!...THERE ARE *FOUR* OF US GOING ON THIS TRIP!"

"MY TEETH!...I CAN'T FIND MY TEETH!"

"HEATHCLIFF WON 'BEST SMILE IN SHOW'!"

"DON'T MAKE SUCH A BIG DEAL OUT OF
A LOST GOLF BALL!"

"WHAT'S HE DOING AT THE HEAD OF THE PARADE ?!!"

"YES...?"

"I DON'T NEED AN ASSISTANT!"

"STRIKE THREE!...YOU'RE OUT!"

"WHO'D LIKE TO GO TO THE ANTIQUE CAR SHOW?!"

"I HATE TO BREAK UP YOUR BEACH PARTY, BUT...."

"WELL, THEY'RE NOT GOING TO MAKE ME EAT CROW!"

6-3 1977 McNaught Synd., Inc.

"NOBODY IS GOING TO EAT CROW!"

"YOUR DAD NEVER VISITS FOR LONG."